IN SEARCH OF YOUR IMAGE

M000205159

A Practical Guide To The

Mental and Spiritual

Aspects Of Horsemanship

◆

WORKBOOK

Jill Keiser Hassler

edited by Jessica Jahiel
illustrated by Jeanette Manley and Emily Covington
front cover art by Eleanor McDonald
back cover art by Jeanette Manley

© Copyright 1993 by Jill Keiser Hassler
All Rights Reserved

Published by:

  Goals Unlimited Press
  C/O Hilltop Farm, Inc.
  1089 Nesbitt Road
  Colora, MD 21917

Production by:

  Mountain Press Publishing Company
  P.O. Box 2399
  Missoula, Montana 59806

Printed in the United States of America

ISBN #0-9632562-4-6 $12.95

I dedicate this Workbook, with graditude, to the following:

The horses, students and professionals who have provided me with experiential learning, open communications and continual feedback.

The devoted, hard working Hilltop staff for their understanding, communication, dedication and responsibility that provided me with the time and mental freedom to write.

The productive and successful lives of my children, Patti, Chip and Scott as well as the many other young people who grew up in our extended family. Their lives have given me the confidence to put my thoughts into words.

The new friends who provided my mountain top for writing, my Montana home: Sharon Gordon who searched with dediction until she found the perfect homesite, to Dr. Earl Pruyn who was willing to sell his unlisted land, and to Ed McHatton who built the perfect house to capture the nature that so energizes me.

Vonnie Groff who provided the inspiration and hope to pursue spiritual development.

Jeanette Manley and Emily Covington for their illustrative ideas and art work.

Jessica Jahiel who called at just the right moment and then shared her editing skills and quick-mindedness!

Jane Mac Elree, owner of Hilltop Farm, who has provided a place for my dreams to make a difference. She has trusted me to manage Hilltop while writing in Montana. Jane's vision, intelligence, dedication and compassion have made her an inspirational role model to me.

Russell Scoop who exposed me to a new awareness and has continued his support with endless hours of discussions, reading and editing. Every page has passed before his eyes at least three times!

A special dedication to each reader, wishing you an inspiring journey.

_____

Reader's Signature

Beginning Date _____

TABLE OF CONTENTS

IN SEARCH OF YOUR IMAGE WORKBOOK

Before you begin this Workbook, be certain that you have read *In Search Of Your Image* from cover to cover. Your reading will have laid the foundation for the process you are about to begin. As you read, make a note of anything that makes you feel confused, uncertain, questioning, or curious. When you have finished the book, look at your list and decide what issues you would like to begin with. That is where you should begin in the Workbook.

Once you decide where you want to begin, re-read the chapter or section in *In Search Of Your Image*. Now it is time to begin your personal journey.

Both the book and the workbook are designed to help you learn to use goals to help create peace, harmony, joy, and confidence in your life. This is a slow process. Give yourself time.

While you are working in the Workbook, you may discover areas that hold a special interest for you. Use the long-term, intermediate, and short-term goal planning to master the tasks of your choice. Your long-term goal will be the area you want to improve, your intermediate goal will be your regular plan for practicing the exercise, and your short-term goal will be the act of performing the exercise using both your critical and your reflective thinking processes, until the new skill becomes natural to you.

Just as there is no right or wrong way to think, there is no right or wrong order in which to use this Workbook. It is your personal book, and you should feel free to use it in ANY WAY and in ANY ORDER that feels right to you.

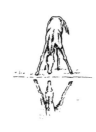

Basic Workbook Rules:
- *1. Read all of* In Search Of Your Image *before you begin.*
- *2. Re-read related book section or chapter as you use charts, exercises and questionnaires.*
- *3. Repeat charts, exercises and questionnaires as often as you need to get a clear picture.*
- *4. Work on ONE issue at a time.*
- *5. Redo your entire Workbook in a year and enjoy what you discover!*

This Workbook can become an annual journal in which you record your progress. Many chapters will inspire a new awareness in you, and during the year you will change and grow without even thinking about it. You will find it very interesting to see the changes that will take place in you from year to year. In addition, journal-keeping is a valuable tool for busy people; you can always go back and review situations, feelings and thoughts.

Enjoy your personal journey, and read on . . .

GOALS

Goals give a purpose and direction to your journey through life with your horses. Setting goals is not a mysterious process, but it does take a little work and forethought. This Workbook section is designed to help those who are willing to dedicate some time and thought to the process of recognizing and planning their goals.

The charts and questionnaires that accompany the Motivation section will help readers take a serious look at their personal motivation. There are no charts or questionnaires accompanying the Stages chapter, because your stage will be very obvious to you as you read the chapter. Outside influences may have more effect than you recognize, so there are charts to help you evaluate these aspects of your life. Last but not least is the actual process of choosing goals. The questionnaires offered in this section of the Workbook should help you put together what you have learned while studying this section of the book.

You may wish to copy charts #1-5 before you begin. These charts should be repeated to give you the maximum practice and information.

Before you begin the Workbook, you should have read all of *In Search Of Your Image*, and just before you begin the exercises, charts or questionnaires, you should re-read the section of *In Search Of Your Image* on pages 5-62. It will add more meaning to your work.

In my own journey, I often discovered that I wished I had a blank chart for future use. If you wish to use charts repeatedly, please feel free to make additional copies of what you need.

Enjoy your journey!

GOALS-MOTIVATION

Questionnaire #1

WHY DO I RIDE? Please take a moment and consider all the reasons that you are involved with horses. Write what first comes to you, including all the reasons that you can think of. If you have reasons not listed, that is fine. The motivation suggestions to consider are: Love of horses, exercise, challenge, profession, recreation, companionship, social interaction, and mental well-being.

Date:_____

The first thought that comes to me when I ask myself the question, "Why do I ride?"

_____

_____

_____

_____

_____

_____

_____

_____

_____

_____

_____

_____

GOALS-MOTIVATION

Motivation Chart #1

Circle the importance of each of the following motivations in your life at this time. 1 = not important at all, 2 = slightly important, 3 = moderately important, 4 = very important, and 5 = MOST important. Once you have rated each of the categories, add up your total score.

Date:_____

Love of Horses	1	2	3	4	5
Exercise	1	2	3	4	5
Challenge	1	2	3	4	5
Professional	1	2	3	4	5
Companionship and Social Interaction	1	2	3	4	5
Mental well-being	1	2	3	4	5

total per column _____

grand total _____

If your grand total score is over 21, it means that horses are very important to you, and play a major role in your life. You must find a way to be very involved with them. Read on for further sorting.

If your grand total score is between 14 and 21, horses play an important role in your life, but you do not need a major involvement, although you need some regular involvement.

If your grand total score is below 14, you should enjoy horses but you do not need too much involvement.

GOALS-MOTIVATION

Questionnaire #2

Date: _____

Love of Horses

1. How do horses make you feel when around them?
    _____fulfilled
    _____warm
    _____comfortable
    _____energized

2. How much do you miss horses when you are away?
    _____not at all
    _____a little
    _____a lot

Exercise

3. How much time do you spend on exercise a week?
    _____1hr _____2hrs _____3hrs _____4hrs
    _____5hrs _____6hrs _____7hrs _____8hrs
    _____more

4. Importance of exercise to you
    _____not at all
    _____moderately
    _____very important

5. How completely does your horse activity meet your exercise needs?
    _____not at all
    _____moderately
    _____completely

Professional

6. Rate your profession.
    _____do not like it
    _____like it moderately
    _____love it

7. Rate your desire to go to work daily.
    _____dislike to get up and go to work
    _____push myself a lot but enjoy when I get there
    _____love my work

Recreation

8. Rate the refreshment of your horse activity time.
_____not energized at all
_____moderately energized
_____energized, feel much better

9. Rate recreation value of horses to your life.
_____not recreation
_____slight recreation
_____take up my recreation time
_____my only recreation

10. Amount of recreation time per week with horses.
_____1hr _____2hrs _____3hrs _____4hrs
_____5hrs _____6hrs _____7hrs _____8hrs
_____more

Companionship and Social Activity

11. Rate the companionship provided by horses.
_____none
_____little
_____moderate
_____a lot

12. Rate the value of the interaction with the people involved in the activity.
_____none
_____little
_____moderate
_____a lot

13. Rate the sharing of communications and activities with other like-minded people.
_____upsetting
_____has no effect
_____stimulating
_____satisfying

14. Rate the following in order of one to three [three being most important].
_____activity _____horses _____people involved

Mental Well-Being

15. Rate the sense of understanding yourself by understanding horses.
_____none
_____a little
_____a lot

16. Rate the sense of understanding yourself by being involved with horse people.
_____none
_____a little
_____a lot

17. Rate your horse time's stimulation of 'food for thought'.
_____not at all
_____a little
_____a lot

18. Rate how you feel inside when you leave the horses and return to your 'everyday life'.
_____confused
_____not confused
_____refreshed

GOALS-OUTSIDE INFLUENCES

Chart #2

Financial Evaluation   **Date:** _____

Monthly figures:

Income:

     Salary   _____

     Interest   _____

     Dividends   _____

     Other   _____

                 _____

                 _____

     TOTAL   _____

Expenses:

     Food   _____   [$200.00/month/person=average]

     Loans   _____

                 _____

                 _____

     Medical   _____   [$75.00/month/person=average]

     Insurance   _____

     Utilities   _____

     Housing   _____

     Taxes   _____

     Transportation   _____

     Phone   _____

     Entertainment   _____

     Personal   _____   [hair cut/dry cleaning]

     Clothing   _____

     Repairs   _____

     Education   _____

     Horse   _____

     TOTAL   _____

Further breakdown for horse activities:

Instruction	_____
Training	_____
Feed or Board	_____
Farrier	_____
Vet	_____
Tack & Equip	_____
Riding Clothes	_____
Horse Transp	_____
Show fees	_____
Transp to show	_____
TOTAL	_____

GOALS-OUTSIDE INFLUENCES
Chart #3

Energy Evaluation   Month _____

Please fill in the following chart daily for at least one month. Using a check mark, identify how your mental and physical energy feels during your horse activities.

	Physical Energy			Mental Energy		
	uses little	uses much	creates	uses little	uses much	creates
1						
2						
3						
4						
5						
6						
7						
8						
9						
10						
11						
12						
13						
14						
15						
16						
17						
18						
19						
20						
21						
22						
23						
24						
25						
26						
27						
28						
29						
30						
31						
total						

Total the columns, and you will get an overview of your energy involvement.

GOALS-OUTSIDE INFLUENCES

Chart #4

Time Chart   **Month** _____

Record the time spent in a 24 hour period. Use increments of 1/4 hours. Calculations are best made if you record by .25 (1/4 hr) - .50 (1/2 hr) -.75 (3/4 hr) and 1 hour & up.

	Job	Family	School	Recreation	Horses	Other	Personal	T=24
1								
2								
3								
4								
5								
6								
7								
8								
9								
10								
11								
12								
13								
14								
15								
16								
17								
18								
19								
20								
21								
22								
23								
24								
25								
26								
27								
28								
29								
30								
31								
total								

The totals of this chart will give you some idea of how you spend your time. Please remember that you can personalize it. There is a blank time chart included for your personal use: Chart #5.

GOALS-OUTSIDE INFLUENCES

Chart #5

Personal Time Chart   Date:_____

Create categories based on what you need to know about your life. See next page for a sample time chart from one of the months of my life. Customize this chart to match the time requirements of your life during a month. This time chart can be a valuable aid to you, and help you to make the necessary adjustments in your life.

							T=24
1							
2							
3							
4							
5							
6							
7							
8							
9							
10							
11							
12							
13							
14							
15							
16							
17							
18							
19							
20							
21							
22							
23							
24							
25							
26							
27							
28							
29							
30							
31							
T=							

GOALS-OUTSIDE INFLUENCES

Chart #5

Personal Time Chart   Hilltop   Date: 8/93

	T.H.	T.A.	T.Tv.	Farm Wk.	Manage ofc	Book	General	Teach	
1					6	4			
2	4				10				
3	3				14				
4					13				
5	5				7				
6					11	2			
7					6	4			
8								9.5	Allentown 4 hrs travel
9	5							4.5	Delaware 1.5 hrs. Travel
10	3								
11					14				
12	6								
13					15				
14					6				New York
15						4			Fly to MT/Book review
16					1	14			⎫ Back To
17					1	16			⎬
18					1	15			⎭ Mtn. Press
19					3	16			
20					1	2	7		
21					−			4.5	⎫ MT lessons ½ hr. Dr.
22					−			5.25	⎬ ½ hr Dr
23					3		4		Bill Paying
24					4				
25					12				Travel to MD
26	2				15				
27	7				3				⎫ Clinic
28	12				2				⎬
29	10				6				
30					11.5			4	Delaware 1.5 travel
31						8			Fly to MT-WB
T=	Teach Hilltop	Teach Away	Teach Travel	Teach Work	Farm Work	Management			

GOALS-CHOOSING GOALS

Questionnaire #3

Recording Your Dreams (long-term Goal)

Questions 1 and 2 can be filled out now. Questions 3 and 4 on the next page should be filled out after you discover your mountain top, so that you can use it. After discovering your mountain top, go back to questions 3 and 4, and answer them before reviewing your answers to questions 1 and 2. This is part of the self-discovery process. You will have fun reviewing this exercise.

1. A list of all my horse-related wishes.   Date:_____

2. A list of my realistic horse-related wishes.   Date:_____

These lists should be made after meditating on your mountain top.

Date:_____

3. My list of ALL my horse dreams (wishes) after my mountain top brainstorming session.

Date:_____

4. My list of realistic wishes after my mountain top brainstorming session.

GOALS-CHOOSING GOALS

Questionnaire #4

Goals Worksheet

Your long-term goal will determine the number of intermediate goals that you need to make. This, in turn, will affect the number of short-term goals that you need to reach. While long-term and intermediate goals create the road map, you cannot pre-determine the time your journey will take because you do not know the number of roadblocks that can get in your way. This basic plan gives you a map to help you move forward. I have broken goal-setting into three categories, but you can see how having a daily goal to meet one of your short-term steps will be invaluable to your progress.

(Sample)   Date:_____

1. My main riding motivation is:

2. My second highest motivation is:

3. My stage of life is:

4. My budget for horse activity is:

5. My energy evaluation conclusion is:

6. My time demands allow me to devote_____time to horses.

7. My most realistic dream is:

My Personal Riding Goals Road Map

1. Long-term goal

2. Intermediate goals to attain long-term goal:

1.	7.
2.	8.
3.	9.
4.	10.
5.	11.
6.	12.

3. Short term goal (each of the steps of intermediate goal have short term goals.

• Intermediate goal 1(from question #2 of Personal Goals Road Map)

        Step 1

        Step 2

        Step 3

        Step 4

        Step 5

        Step 6

• Intermediate goal 2(from question #2 of Personal Goals Road Map)

        Step 1

        Step 2

        Step 3

        Step 4

        Step 5

        Step 6

• Intermediate goal 3

        Step 1

        Step 2

        Step 3

        Step 4

        Step 5

        Step 6

◆ Intermediate goal 4

> Step 1
>
> Step 2
>
> Step 3
>
> Step 4
>
> Step 5
>
> Step 6

◆ Intermediate goal 5

> Step 1
>
> Step 2
>
> Step 3
>
> Step 4
>
> Step 5
>
> Step 6

◆ Intermediate goal 6

> Step 1
>
> Step 2
>
> Step 3
>
> Step 4
>
> Step 5
>
> Step 6

UNDERSTANDING HORSE AND MAN

Understanding your horse is easy; understanding yourself is very difficult. Few of us understand very much about our own being. Like horsemastership, it is a lifelong pursuit. For most of us, the balance of our own being and its relationship to the Universe is something that we either avoid looking at or take for granted. Seeking to understand and love ourselves is the first step that we often hear about. But how do we do it? Those of us who are horse lovers are one step ahead because our horses can serve as our teachers and role models.

I am offering the seven questionnaires in this section to inspire you to take a deep look inside yourself and your horse. The questions may help you to accept and understand yourself better.

It is important for you to re-read the Understanding section of *In Search Of Your Image* found on pages 63-134 before you complete this section.

UNDERSTANDING—HORSE-PHYSICAL

Questionnaire #1

Horse Physical Evaluation   **Date:** _____

Please evaluate your horse's conformation and movement. Rate 1-3 [1 = problem, 2 = minor problem, 3 = good]. If your score is below 3, describe the specific fault/problem.

Area to rate	Description	Rating
Proportion/Balance		
Front [head - withers]		_____
Back [withers - hip]		_____
Hind [hip - buttocks]		_____
Legs		
Front legs: straightness		_____
Front legs: proportion		_____
Hind legs: straightness		_____
Hind legs: proportion		_____
Movement [observe without rider]		
Overall freedom		_____
Freedom in back		_____
Freedom in forehand		_____
Freedom in hindleg		_____
Unsoundness		
Internal [lungs, eyes, heart]		_____
Hindleg		_____
Frontleg		_____
Stiffness [list cause: age, illness, training, rider]		
Forehand		_____
Back		_____
Hindquarters		_____
Horse Care		
Regular schedule		_____
Individualized feeding program		_____
Regular veterinary care		_____
Regular dental care		_____
Regular farrier care		_____
Well-monitored freedom [pasture]		_____
Regular grooming		_____
Well-kept and ventilated stall		_____

Total

1. Long-term goal with the horse you evaluated.

2. Physical requirements of horse to meet your goal.

3. Your horse's limitations and problems.

4. The limitations or problems of your horse as they relate to your goals.

5. Is my horse physically suited for my goals?_____yes _____no.

   If NO, a list of options I can consider.

UNDERSTANDING—MAN-PHYSICAL

Questionnaire #2

My Personal Evaluation   **Date:** _____

Please evaluate your body's proportions and its relationship to your goals. Rate 1-3 [1 = problem, 2 = minor problem, 3 = good]. If you rate yourself below 3, describe the problem/fault.

Area to rate	**Description**	**Rating**
Proportion/Balance		
Height to weight		_____
Upper body to lower body		_____
Proportion of Body Parts		
Upper arm		_____
Lower arm		_____
Thigh		_____
Lower leg		_____
Length of neck		_____
Width of shoulders		_____
Width of hips		_____
Weight		
Overall weight		_____
Weight of upper body		_____
Weight of buttocks		_____
Weight of thighs		_____
Weight of lower legs		_____
Physical Stiffness		
Spine		_____
Shoulders		_____
Elbows		_____
Wrists		_____
Fingers		_____
Neck		_____
Lower back		_____
Hip joints		_____
Knees		_____
Ankles		_____
	Total	_____

1. What I really like about my body.

2. What I do not like about my body.

3. What I can change about what I do not like.

4. My plan to change what I can change.

5. What I cannot change about what I do not like.

6. The effect on my riding of what I cannot change.

7. Will what I cannot change affect my goal with my horse?

8. If so, how?

9. If it will affect my goal, what can I do about it?

10. Methods I can use to begin to accept what I cannot change.

UNDERSTANDING—HORSE-MENTAL

Questionnaire #3

Horse-Mental Evaluation   Date: _____

Like most of the questionnaires, this questionnaire is not designed to determine whether something is "right" or "wrong". The ratings are designed to help you evaluate your horse's mental characteristics. Please rate each from 1 - 3 according to each area's requests. If you score below three, please describe.

Area to rate	Description	Rating
Basic Characteristics [1 = not important, 2 = average importance, 3 = important]		
Leadership		_____
Control		_____
Routine		_____
Social interaction		_____
Sensory Perception [1 = little influence, 2 = average influence, 3 = very influenced]		
Smell		_____
Taste		_____
Sight		_____
Hearing		_____
Feel		
Emotions [1 = little demonstration, 2 = average demonstration, 3 = very demonstrative]		
Fear		_____
Anger		_____
Joy		_____
Surprise		_____
Other [1 = exhibits little, 2 = average, 3 = exhibits a lot]		
Intelligence		_____
Patience		_____
Expectations		_____

UNDERSTANDING—MAN-MENTAL

Questionnaire #4

Examining Thoughts

This questionnaire asks you to first identify the issue. To solve a problem, you will first deconstruct it piece by piece. Next, you will examine the areas you least understand; and finally, you will reconstruct the issue with your NEW understanding, which should lead you to a decision or solution. Notice how you must consider both yourself and your horse in this process. You may wish to copy this questionnaire to use again and again, or you may wish to wait and try this process after you have learned more. This process can become automatic, and you will then have an asset that can really help you to better understand and solve problems. See next page for sample. Re-reading pages 108-109 in Man Mental Chapter will help.[* See sample Questionnaire #4 on page 27]

Date:_____

Description of situation or issue of concern.

Deconstruction:	**Evaluation:**	**Reconstruction:**

Physical Aspects:

• Structure of horse

• Structure of man

• Care of horse

• Care of man

Mental Aspects:

• Leadership:
    Horse:

    Man:

• Control:
    Horse:

    Man:

• Routine:
    Horse:

    Man:

◆ Social Interaction:
    Horse:

    Man:

◆ Intelligence:
    Horse:

    Man:

◆ Sensual perception:
    Horse:

    Man:

◆ Patience:
    Horse:

    Man:

◆ Expectations:
    Horse:

    Man:

Spiritual Aspects:
◆ Love:
    Horse:

    Man:

◆ Energy:
    Horse:

    Man:

◆ Attitude:
    Horse:

    Man:

A description of the issue after this process.

* Sample Questionnaire #4

Problem:
Slim has been foxhunting for years, but during this season Pandy, his hunter, has begun stopping at the fences in the hunt field.

	Deconstruct	Evaluate	Reconstruct
Physical-Pandy long back/15 yrs old		soreness?	possible lameness
Physical-Slim broke knee skiing last winter		tightness?	possible stiffness
Care of Pandy	good		
Care of Slim	good		
Mental			
Leadership-Pandy	non-aggressive	passive	no stimulation
Leadership-Slim	wants to be in front	over-rides	may be interfering
Control-Pandy	passive	happy to follow	
Control-Slim	wants to show off	very aggressive	may be interfering
Routine-Pandy	needs regular work	may not be getting	may be weak
Routine-Slim	hates	rides occasionally	may be unfit
Social Interaction-Pandy	loves other horses	loves group	doesn't like to leave group
Social Interaction-Slim	loves to show off	loves to lead	may be over-riding
Intelligence-Pandy	low level	happy to follow	non-aggressive
Intelligence-Slim	average	has a good time	does not think
Sensual Perception-Pandy	high	herd instinct strong	does not like to leave other horses
Sensual Perception-Slim	slight	doesn't notice much	
Patience-Pandy	very patient	puts up with as much as he can	
Patience-Slim	impatient	wants action at will	creates aggression
Expectations-Pandy	average	enjoys hunt itself	
Expectations-Slim	very high	expects unfit horse to run and jump	unrealistic
Spiritual			
Love-Pandy	unconditional	will try to please	
Love-Slim	conditional	based on performance	horse/mechanical
Energy-Pandy	average		
Energy-Slim	high	for what he wants	needs to redirect
Attitude-Pandy	positive/ears always up except at jump		
Attitude-Slim	positive/except when refuses	blames Pandy	could be a reason there

A description of the issue after this process.

   If Slim would stop and review both his knee injury and Pandy's lack of condition for his age, he might uncover his problem. The refusals could be from pain from lack of condition in Pandy, or from Slim's own knee injury which could have caused a balance problem which is affecting Pandy's balance. Slim needs to engage his empathy and use his intelligence to look more deeply and try to resolve the problem so he does not continue to get embarrassed with his friends.

UNDERSTANDING—MAN-MENTAL

Questionnaire #5

Expectations

Answering the following questions will help you review and compare your expectations and those of your horse.

Date:_____

A Day's Ride

1. What I expect out of today's ride.

2. When did I begin thinking about today's ride?

3. What I think my horse expects out of today's ride.

4. When did my horse begin thinking about today's ride?

5. How did my expectations compare with the results of the day's ride?

6. How did I create my expectations of today's ride?

A Competition

1. What do I expect out of the competition?

2. When did I begin thinking seriously about the competition?

3. What do I think that my horse expects out of the competition?

4. When does my horse begin thinking about the competition?

5. How did my expectations compare to the competition itself?

6. How did I create the expectations for the competition?

UNDERSTANDING—MAN-MENTAL

Questionnaire #6

My Mental Make-up

This may be the most difficult questionnaire in this Workbook. Don't worry if you cannot answer a question. Answer what you can, and leave what is unknown until later. This is part of taking a serious look at your own mental make-up, to help you recognize where your strengths and weaknesses lie.

Date:_____

1. How do I learn best? [1 = little influence, 2 = average, 3 = a lot]
   Seeing   _____
   Hearing   _____
   Reading   _____
   Repetition   _____

2. My emotional expression [1 = not often, 2 = average, 3 = frequently]
   Cry   _____
   Laugh   _____
   Become silent   _____
   Become verbally aggressive   _____
   Become physically aggressive   _____
   Turn to alcohol or drugs   _____

3. Emotions affecting me [1 = not often, 2 = sometimes, 3 = frequently]
   Happiness   _____
   Boredom   _____
   Antagonism   _____
   Anger   _____
   Hostility   _____
   Fear   _____
   Grief   _____
   Dejection   _____
   Apathy   _____

4. My basic thinking process [1 = never, 2 = sometimes, 3 = often]
   My first thoughts are negative   _____
   My first thoughts are positive   _____
   I feel challenged by new thoughts   _____
   I feel overwhelmed by new thoughts   _____
   I avoid thinking   _____
   I look for things to think about   _____
   I challenge authoritative thinking   _____
   I submit to authoritative thinking   _____

I find it easy to think from other's point of view _____
I find it difficult to think from other's point of view _____
I am open-minded _____
I am closed-minded _____

5. How I react [1 = never, 2 = sometimes, 3 = often]
   Quickly _____
   Slowly _____
   Afraid of making a mistake _____
   Without thought _____
   Thinking first _____
   Based on emotion _____
   Based on thought _____

6. What affects my ability to feel [1 = never, 2 = sometimes, 3 = often]
   Being with others _____
   Being alone _____
   Music _____
   Rain _____
   Light _____
   Noise _____
   Quiet _____
   Water _____
   Darkness _____

   _____ _____

   _____ _____

7. What affects my feelings [1 = never, 2 = sometimes, 3 = often]
   People's reactions _____
   The environment _____
   My mood _____
   People's words _____
   Results of my own actions _____
   My horse's reactions _____
   Criticism _____

8. How I feel around horses [1 = never, 2 = sometimes, 3 = often]
   Good while working around them _____
   Bad while working around them _____
   Good when taking care of their needs _____
   Irritated or bored when taking care of their needs _____
   Good about the cost related to them _____
   Irritated about the costs _____
   Good while riding _____
   Irritated or unhappy while riding _____
   Energized by time with horse _____
   Frustrated by time with horse

UNDERSTANDING—MAN-SPIRITUAL

Questionnaire #7

Role Of Spirit

It is hard for us to identify our spirit. These few questions will set the stage for a deeper view of your inner being. Answer what you can, and come back later to the questions you cannot answer now.

Date:_____

1.   Who are the people in your life that project a sense of honesty, sincerity and compassion? What gives you this feeling?

2.   Have you ever had an unexplainable coincidence occur in your life? Describe it.

3.   Have you ever had thoughts that seem illogical or out of place, that you push back and try not to listen to? Describe.

4.   What role does your conscience play in your life?

5.   What role does your intuition play in your life?

6.   What role does prayer play in your life?

7.   What is the role of religion in your life?

8.   What is your perception of spirit, related to your religious beliefs?

9.   Rate the following [1 = seldom, 2 = sometimes, 3 = often]
     Love gives a feeling of awe   _____
     Love gives a feeling of unity   _____
     Love gives a feeling of peace   _____
     Love gives a feeling of sadness   _____
     Love gives a feeling of loneliness   _____

10. Have energy to do what I like   _____
     Have energy to do what I do not like   _____
     Have energy to be creative   _____
     Feel energized from physical activity   _____
     Feel energy from horse activities   _____
     Feel energy from being around a horse   _____
     Feel energy from sleep   _____
     Feel energy from a ride   _____
     Feel energy from nature   _____
     Feel energy from within self   _____
     Feel energy from achievement   _____

11. Have a positive view of self   _____
     Have a positive view of horse   _____
     Have a positive view of environment   _____
     Have a positive view of people around me   _____
     Have a positive view of what I am doing   _____
     Have a positive view of a negative situation   _____
     View personal life with negativity   _____
     View horse life negatively   _____
     View self negatively   _____
     View environment negatively   _____

12. What do you see as the life force within you and your horse?

13. What is the most basic reason for a horse's kindness, acceptance and power?

RESOURCES

The exercises, charts, and questionnaires in this section of the Workbook are designed to help you learn to recognize and develop your gifts of love and energy, to nurture your attitude, humility, empathy, and forgiveness, and to help you recognize and use your tools: concentration, knowledge, relaxation, mountain top, on hold, discipline, commitment, patience, praise, and imagery.

The exercises should be practiced one at a time, as often as necessary, until you discover that they have become easy. Once this happens, you are likely to use them without thinking about them: this is your goal.

The charts are designed to record your activities over a month. You may wish to do them more often. Seldom do you learn in one month all that you want and need to know. I suggest you copy the charts to record several months.

The questionnaires will ask you to recall experiences. Try to answer the questions with a clear mind, recalling as much as you can. Initially you may wish to go to your mountain top to answer the questions. Copy the questionnaires and re-answer 3-6 months after the first month; this is a good way for you to document your growth.

As with all the other sections of this Workbook, before practicing an exercise or completing a chart or questionnaire you should first re-read the chapter pertaining to the exercise, chart or questionnaire.

Please do these one at a time, or they will lose their effectiveness. Go forward and have fun!

RESOURCES

Questionnaire #1

Personal Love Evaluation   Date: _____

1. List what you like about your body.

2. List what you do not like about your body.

3. What CAN I change that I do not like?

4. What can I NOT change that I do not like?

5. Why do I dislike the above-mentioned characteristics?

6. What effect do these characteristics have on my life?

7. What can I do to accept what I cannot change?

8. Can or should I rearrange my goals?

Personal Love Evaluation

Date: _____

1. List what you like about your body.

2. List what you do not like about your body.

3. What CAN I change that I do not like?

4. What can I NOT change that I do not like?

5. Why do I dislike the above-mentioned characteristics?

6. What effect do these characteristics have on my life?

7. What can I do to accept what I cannot change?

8. Can or should I rearrange my goals?

RESOURCES

Questionnaire #2

Mental Love Evaluation   **Date:** _____

1. List what you LIKE about yourself mentally.

2. List what you DO NOT LIKE about yourself mentally.

3. What can I CHANGE that I DO NOT like?

4. What can I NOT CHANGE that I DO NOT like?

5. Why do I dislike the above-mentioned characteristics?

6. What effects do these characteristics have on my life?

7. What can I do to accept what I cannot change?

8. Can and should I rearrange my goals?

RESOURCES

Questionnaire #3

Spiritual Love Evaluation

Date: _____

1. Describe what you consider to be your spirit.

2. I feel my spiritual love [1 = seldom, 2 = average, 3 = often]
    I love my own horse _____
    I feel a deep compassion for most horses _____
    A special feeling comes over me around horses _____
    I am drawn to horses _____
    I feel a bond with most people _____
    I accept my inner feelings _____
    I feel a responsibility to more than myself _____
    I feel better when around a horse _____
    I feel more comfortable around a horse _____
    I feel more appreciated around a horse _____
    I feel energized around a horse _____

    I express myself [1 = not easily, 2 = easily, 3 = very easily]
    Through crying _____
    Through laughter _____
    Through hugging _____
    Through touching _____
    Through words _____

4. What makes you WONDER about the universe?

5. What is your religious philosophy?

6. What do you consider the connection between your religion and your spirit?

7. What is the role of religion in your life?

8. All the methods of expressing ourselves should be used. All, with the exception of talking, can be part of spiritual expression [not romantic love]. Do you feel that you use the others to honestly express your innermost feelings? If not, which would you like to work on?

chart on second side/six months later

Spiritual Love Evaluation   **Date:** _____

1.   Describe what you consider to be your spirit.

2.   I feel my spiritual love [1 = seldom, 2 = average, 3 = often]
     I love my own horse   _____
     I feel a deep compassion for most horses   _____
     A special feeling comes over me around horses   _____
     I am drawn to horses   _____
     I feel a bond with most people   _____
     I accept my inner feelings   _____
     I feel a responsibility to more than myself   _____
     I feel better when around a horse   _____
     I feel more comfortable around a horse   _____
     I feel more appreciated around a horse   _____
     I feel energized around a horse   _____

     I express myself [1 = not easily, 2 = easily, 3 = very easily]
     Through crying   _____
     Through laughter   _____
     Through hugging   _____
     Through touching   _____
     Through words   _____

4.   What makes you WONDER about the universe?

5.   What is your religious philosophy?

6.   What do you consider the connection between your religion and your spirit?

7.   What is the role of religion in your life?

8.   All the methods of expressing ourselves should be used. All, with the exception of talking, can be part of spiritual expression [not romantic love]. Do you feel that you use the others to honestly express your innermost feelings? If not, which would you like to work on?

RESOURCES-ENERGY

Questionnaire #4

Mental Roadblock Diary   **Date** _____

Think of an experience that caused you considerable pain. Write down the experience, and then try to evaluate your reactions. Check the action that most closely describes your response.

Experience: **Cause:**

1. Emotion experienced
   joy _____
   anger _____
   jealousy _____
   confusion _____
   sadness _____

2. What I did?
   ignored _____
   thought _____
   acted immediately_____
   acted after thought _____

3. What was solved?
   nothing _____
   had to accept _____
   understood better _____
   I overreacted _____
   I feel better _____
   I feel worse _____

4. Did I experience thoroughly?

5. Is the original issue completely resolved?

6. If not, what remains unresolved?

RESOURCES-ENERGY

Questionnaire #5

Communication Roadblock Diary   **Date:** _____

Think of a communication experience with another person that caused you uncomfortable feelings. Write it down, and then check the answer or feeling that best describes how you acted or felt.

Experience: **Cause:**
1. Communication experience
    satisfied _____
    confused _____
    angered _____

2. What I did
    ignored _____
    thought about it _____
    looked at it from the other
    person's point of view _____
    reacted immediately _____
    responded after thought _____
    had a fight _____
    became quietly angry _____

3. What was solved?
    nothing _____
    understood _____
    more confused _____
    more angry _____
    feel better _____
    feel worse _____

4. Did I carefully view the other point of view with an open and clear mind?

5. Was the original communication resolved?

6. If not, what remains confusing or anger-creating?

7. How can I deal with the left over feelings?

RESOURCES-ENERGY

Questionnaire #6

Understanding Your Intuition   **Date:** _____

These questions may help you discover your hidden intuition, a valuable source of personal information. Intuition is often repressed and locked away, therefore you may not recognize anything new when you answer these questions. They are designed to start the process. Stop for a few minutes, and recall answers to the following questions as best you can.

1. Describe a hunch that you had.

2. Did you have verification of the hunch?

3. Describe a gut-feeling that you have experienced.

4. Did the gut-feeling have any later verification? If so, describe.

5. Did you ever feel that you had been to a place before but you could not remember it? If so, describe.

6. Have you ever felt that you had known a person before, but you could not remember where or when? If so, describe.

7. Have you ever had a thought or dream come true for what appeared to be no reason? If yes, write a short description.

RESOURCES-ENERGY

Exercise #1

Intuition Stimulation

This simple exercise may help you to become more totally involved in each experience that you have. While this exercise may take you several minutes while you are learning it, with practice it will become an instinctive action that will require no conscious effort.

1.   Go to a quiet place in your mind. This usually requires some form of meditation. If you have none, return to this after you have read the Relaxation chapter.

2.   Continue to breathe deeply, and remain quiet in your mind.

3.   Go through your body; spend a few minutes on each activity
        smell your body from head to foot, part by part
        feel your body from head to foot, part by part
        listen to your breathing
        with your eyes closed, view your body, part by part

4.   Now take a thought, any thought. Perhaps you have a simple decision like which ring to ride your horse in today.
        feel yourself and your horse in each ring
        feel the footing in each ring
        smell the air in each ring
        feel the breeze, stillness, or wind in each ring
        listen to the sounds in each ring
        see the environment of each ring

5. Allow yourself to experience this in your relaxed state.

6. Write down what your conclusion was and why.

RESOURCES-ENERGY

Chart #1

Meditation Chart   **Month:**_____ **Year:**_____

This Chart is designed to help you develop the habit of using meditation, and to help you realize the effect it can produce. The time should be recorded in quarter hour blocks [15min. = .25, 30 min. = .50, 45 min. = .75 and 60 min. = 1hr.]. Your description should be noted with numbers or abbreviations [1 = worse, 2 = same, 3 = better].

	Type	Time	Feel Before	Feel After
1				
2				
3				
4				
5				
6				
7				
8				
9				
10				
11				
12				
13				
14				
15				
16				
17				
18				
19				
20				
21				
22				
23				
24				
25				
26				
27				
28				
29				
30				
31				

RESOURCES-ENERGY

Chart #2
Diagnostic Chart

Each upsetting experience is connected to a feeling which frequently gets locked away. Identifying the source will help us to know where to begin to look for these hidden feelings. This chart is designed to help you decide where to begin your search, mentally or spiritually. This may save you some time. The x indicates where you may find the source that is connected with the unsettling or upsetting feeling. Describe the upsetting experience and then circle how you feel. This is a starting point.

Date:_____

1. Experience:

	Mental	Spiritual
short-tempered	x	
confused	x	x
irritable	x	x
sad	x	x
depressed	x	
impatient	x	
jealous	x	
lack of energy		x
angry	x	
dislike	x	x
uneasy		x
indecisive	x	x

Date:_____

2. Experience:

	Mental	Spiritual
short-tempered	x	
confused	x	x
irritable	x	x
sad	x	x
depressed	x	
impatient	x	
jealous	x	
lack of energy		x
angry	x	
dislike	x	x
uneasy		x
indecisive	x	x

RESOURCES-ATTITUDE

Questionnaire #7

Attitude Examination   **Date:** _____

Take a few minutes, answer the questions, then look at your check marks. If you have any checks in the right-hand column, it is a good idea to analyze why you feel that way. Change what you can change, and make the most of what you cannot change. The right-hand column signifies a negative attitude.

1. When something goes wrong, what is your first thought?

think about it from
other's point of view _____   blame self _____
                                        blame others _____
                                        blame environ. _____

                                        blame horse _____
                                        pretend it is OK _____

2. How often do you smile?

often _____   seldom _____
                        not at all _____

3. How often do you compliment people?

often _____   seldom _____
                        not at all _____

4. How do you view your family life?

enjoyable _____   boring _____
stimulating _____   frustrating _____
rewarding _____   irritating _____
satisfying _____

5. How do you view your professional or educational life?

enjoyable _____   boring _____
stimulating _____   frustrating _____
rewarding _____   irritating _____
satisfying _____

6. How do you view your horse life?

enjoyable _____   boring _____
stimulating _____   frustrating _____
rewarding _____   irritating _____
satisfying _____

7. How do you view your social life?

enjoyable _____   boring _____
stimulating _____   frustrating _____
rewarding _____   irritating _____
satisfying _____

RESOURCES-ATTITUDE

Questionnaire #8

Situation Evaluation

Describe three situations in your life that you considered negative. In A, describe the situation. In B, describe a way that you could have viewed the same situation positively.

Date:_____

1. A. Situation:

    B. How to view it positively.

Date:_____

2. A. Situation:

    B. How to view it positively.

Date:_____

3. A. Situation:

    B. How to view it positively.

RESOURCES-ATTITUDE

Questionnaire #9

Environmental Evaluation

Rate your environment by placing a checkmark in the category that best describes your feelings about each of the listed areas of your life.

Date:_____

	Excellent	Good	Poor

Home and Family:
Satisfies my need for light
Satisfies my need for noise or quiet
Colors inviting
Family positive
Enjoy work at home
Enjoy leisure at home

Professional or Education:
Satisfies my need for light
Work area satisfies my need for noise or quiet
Colors inviting
Co-workers positive
Co-workers caring
Job or clients
Superiors positive

Horse life:
Stable area clean and neat
Stable area satisfies my need for light
Stable area satisfies my need for noise or quiet
Stable area smells clean
Stable staff caring
Stable staff positive
Stable staff knowledgeable
Riding area clean and neat
Riding area satisfies my need for light
Riding area satisfies my need for noise or quiet
Instructor positive attitude
Instructor caring
Instructor knowledgeable
Instructor's ego
Instructor's teaching ability
Horse enjoyable attitude
Horse's training
Horse's size
Horses's ability

Social life; environment changes
Companions attitude
Companions caring
Companions interests

If you have too many checkmarks in the negative category, reevaluate. Change what you can change and accept what you cannot change, so that you can create positive surroundings. They influence you!

RESOURCES-HUMILITY

Questionnaire #10

Humility Evaluation

This questionnaire has been designed to help you evaluate the role of humility in your life. If you look at the way you think of humility, you may see a need to develop that quality. Please describe past performances with your horse, and answer the accompanying questions.

Date:_____

1. Describe a performance with your horse, either good or bad.

a. What role did you play?

b. What role did your horse play?

c. What role did your instructor/coach play?

d. What role did your friends play?

Date:_____

2. Describe a performance with your horse, either good or bad.

a. What role did you play?

b. What role did your horse play?

c. What role did your instructor/coach play?

d. What role did your friends play?

RESOURCES-HUMILITY

Questionnaire #11

Evaluation of Professional's Humility

Please check the most appropriate answer.

Review the checkmarks, especially those in the right-hand column. If there are too many checkmarks in that column, perhaps you should investigate finding a new professional for the job. You cannot change the humility of a professional. You must decide how their humility affects the quality of their work.

Date:_____

Farrier

accepts advice from other professionals	_____	brags	_____
solicits advice from other professionals	_____	resents suggestions	_____
attends learning seminars	_____	uses 'I' frequently	_____
asks you questions	_____	talks frequently	
asks you your goals for self or horse	_____	about named people	
updates knowledge through reading	_____	or stables	_____

Veterinarian

accepts advice from other professionals	_____	brags	_____
solicits advice from other professionals	_____	resents suggestions	_____
attends learning seminars	_____	uses 'I' frequently	_____
asks you questions	_____	talks frequently	
asks you your goals for self or horse	_____	about named people	
updates knowledge through reading	_____	or stables	_____

Instructor/Trainer

accepts advice from other professionals	_____	brags	_____
solicits advice from other professionals	_____	resents suggestions	_____
attends learning seminars	_____	uses 'I' frequently	_____
asks you questions	_____	talks frequently	
asks you your goals for self or horse	_____	about named people	
updates knowledge through reading	_____	or stables	_____

Feed Supplier

accepts advice from other professionals	_____	brags	_____
solicits advice from other professionals	_____	resents suggestions	_____
attends learning seminars	_____	uses 'I' frequently	_____
asks you questions	_____	talks frequently	
asks you your goals for self or horse	_____	about named people	
updates knowledge through reading	_____	or stables	_____

Dentist

accepts advice from other professionals	_____	brags	_____
solicits advice from other professionals	_____	resents suggestions	_____
attends learning seminars	_____	uses 'I' frequently	_____
asks you questions	_____	talks frequently	
asks you your goals for self or horse	_____	about named people	
updates knowledge through reading	_____	or stables	

RESOURCES-KNOWLEDGE

Questionnaire #12

Horse Experience Learning Profile
[see next page for sample completed learning profile]

Date	Activity	What I Did	What I Had to Know	What I Learned

Horse Experience Learning Profile

Date	Activity	What I Did	What I Had to Know	What I Learned
Apr. 93	Klimke Clinic	Observed	Basics of Horsemanship	Straightness + Rhythm Thoroughness even for FEI riders gave me confidence to insist on for my Students
May 93	Florida lessons	Taught	What I wanted to teach plus be able to determine what the students need to learn	Confidence is The most common missing ingred. in many adults; The instructor plays a major role in Confidence building
July 9-11 1993	Dr. Benson's	Supervised & Observed	Rules of Competition How to prepare for Competition + how to organize 16 riders at Competition	Confirmed how young people Think and the role between Their Thoughts, feelings and performance. The role of competitiveness of The individual
Aug. 26-29 1993	Hilltop Clinic	Taught	What I wanted to teach based on individual needs	The results That can be achieved when I combine teachings with both horse and personal relaxation when you have an open willing attitude among all.

RESOURCES-KNOWLEDGE

Questionnaire #13

Learning Style Evaluation

This exercise MUST be done AFTER you have read the Knowledge chapter. It will help you identify your most frequently used learning style. Once you know this, it will help you to know how best to balance your learning. All three learning styles are required for advanced riding. Go back and study your least-used styles, so that you can create a goal that will help you to develop your weakest style.

Date:_____

Learning Styles

	Use Frequently	Use Seldom	Never Use

Cognitive:
think about theory
comprehend thoroughly
discuss objectives
compare and contrast
evaluate

Psychomotor:
learn by steps
know steps thoroughly
observe model
practice until habit
add one pattern to next
practice any changes
organize all that is learned

Affective:
respond to receiving information
see new information as positive or negative
value what feels right
seek different sources of information
knowledge based on inner feelings

RESOURCES-KNOWLEDGE

Questionnaire #14

Evaluation of Learning Sources

Are you taking advantage of all of your learning sources? This questionnaire will help you look at what you use most frequently. You may find that you are not making use of some resources that are actually readily available to you. In order to monitor your changing use of resources, you may wish to keep this record on a monthly basis. But since most of us are busy, keeping it every two or three months is probably more feasible, and will still provide you with useful information and insights.

Date:_____

	Use Frequently	Use Seldom	Never Use
books			
magazine articles			
discussion			
listening			
watching			
instruction			
horse			
life experience			
clinics			
questions			

Date:_____

	Use Frequently	Use Seldom	Never Use
books			
magazine articles			
discussion			
listening			
watching			
instruction			
horse			
life experience			
clinics			
questions			

Date:_____

	Use Frequently	Use Seldom	Never Use
books			
magazine articles			
discussion			
listening			
watching			
instruction			
horse			
life experience			
clinics			
questions			

RESOURCES-EMPATHY

Exercise #2

Practice Empathy With Your Horse

1. Go to the stable area during a quiet time. Initially you do not want anyone else around.

2. Empty your mind.

3. Try to enjoy smelling the environment.

4. Listen to the stable sounds.

5. Listen to your horse's breathing.

6. Look around and see what he sees.

7. Imagine how he sees his environment.

8. As you continue to follow his breathing, try to imagine how he feels.

9. Enjoy this for a few minutes.

10. Write down your feelings.
First try.

Second try.

Third try.

Fourth try.

Fifth try.

Sixth try.

RESOURCES-EMPATHY

Questionnaire #15

How Does My Horse Feel?

Date:_____

	Enjoys	Does Not Matter	Dislikes
stall			
bedding			
water			
hay			
grain			
looking out window			
other horses			
other animals			
pasture			
neighboring horse			
me, when I come to stall			
grooming			
tacking up			
mounting			
dismounting			
washing			
braiding			
hacking			
ring work			
jumping			
roping			
water crossing			
dentist			
vet			
farrier			
stable workers			
van/trailer			
competitions			
rain			
snow			
sun			
bright light			
darkness			
quietness			
loud noises			
trucks			
cars			
tractors			

RESOURCES-RELAXATION

Exercise #3

Practice RSRT

1. Get into a comfortable position, preferably lying down.

2. Make certain you are warm enough.

3. Take a few minutes to recall all the things on your mind and either write them down or put them 'on hold'.

4. Go to a quiet place in your mind.

5. Commit to a time period to allow yourself to relax and recharge.

6. Take three VERY DEEP breaths.

7. Start with your arms and go downwards:
    I feel heat in my fingers
    I feel heat in my arms
    I feel heat in my shoulders
    I feel heat in my chest
    I feel heat in my abdomen
    I feel heat in my hips
    I feel heat in my thighs
    I feel heat in my calves
    I feel heat in my feet

8. Repeat, starting with your arms
    I feel tingling in my fingers
    I feel tingling in my arms
    I feel tingling in my shoulders
    I feel tingling in my chest
    I feel tingling in my abdomen
    I feel tingling in my hips
    I feel tingling in my thighs
    I feel tingling in my calves
    I feel tingling in my feet

9. Take three more deep breaths.

10. Experience whatever comes to you, let it flow . . .

RESOURCES-RELAXATION

Questionnaire #16

Meditation Choice and Evaluation

Take a few moments to define your choice of meditation and refreshment.
Meditation choice:

Prayer	_____	Yoga	_____
Martial Art	_____	Tai Chi	_____
biofeedback	_____	TM	_____
Relaxation Resp	_____	RSRT	_____
other	_____		

Refreshment choice:

music	_____	sauna	_____
walk	_____	whirlpool	_____
bath	_____	other	_____

Monitor the time you spend and the results of both your daily refreshment and daily meditation for one month.

Month _____   Year _____

day	min. refreshing	feel better	feel same	feel worse	min. meditating	feel better	feel same	feel worse
1								
2								
3								
4								
5								
6								
7								
8								
9								
10								
11								
12								
13								
14								
15								
16								
17								
18								
19								
20								
21								
22								
23								
24								
25								
26								
27								
28								
29								
30								
31								

RESOURCES-CONCENTRATION

Exercise #4

Learning To Concentrate

If you practice Steps 1 - 4 until you can automatically concentrate, concentration will become part of your natural thinking process. At that point, it will require little conscious effort on your part. Once this process becomes natural to you, you will be ready to stop using this exercise. Concentration is a natural tool for you to use.

Step 1-Learning to Concentrate

Choose an object that you like: something small, simple and inanimate. Initially give yourself several minutes to practice this step. Practice daily until it is easy and it takes only a few seconds. Once you can do this, you are ready for the next phase of concentration.

1. Choose an object.

2. Look at, feel, smell, touch, listen to the object for a few minutes.

3. Take a few deep breaths.

4. Concentrate with your eyes open for as long as you can, check time.

5. Empty your mind.

6. Go to a quiet place in your mind.

7. Close your eyes and bring forward a picture of the object in your mind.

8. Repeat the exercise and examine the object using steps 2-7 again. How does the object feel?
    how heavy
    how smooth or rough
    how hard or soft
    how does it smell
    how does it sound
    how does it taste
    what is the temperature

9. Imagine how it would feel to be that object.

10. Give a brief written description of the experience each time you do it.

First try.

Second try.

Third try.

Fourth try.

Fifth try.

Sixth try.

These steps have been designed to be practiced for each new movement learned. This applies to everything: posting, diagonals, leads, canter depart, leg-yielding; anything new learned. This step-by-step procedure will be an invaluable learning technique for your future. Once you get in the habit of efficient concentration, you will follow these steps and discover that it requires no conscious thought. The time it will take for this process to become automatic will depend upon the efficiency and regularity with which you practice using it. The more you practice, the faster you will learn.

Step 2
Concentrate on a riding skill, thinking about it from every aspect. This is a recall of the way your body must perform, using the cognitive information for the position or the aids necessary to do a movement.

Step 3
This stage includes feeling your body as you are thinking about the physical requirements.

1. Choose a situation or movement [like the canter depart].

2. Take a few deep breaths.

3. Close your eyes

4. Empty your mind.

5. Bring forward the situation or movement in your mind.

6. FEEL your own body while you are mentally going over aids.
   FEEL your leg muscles
   FEEL your back muscles
   FEEL your joints
   FEEL your arms
   FEEL your hands
   FEEL your posture
   FEEL your body movements with horse

7. Give a brief written description of what you felt each time you practiced.

First try.

Second try.

Third try.

Fourth try.

Fifth try.

Sixth try.

Step 4

   This step is designed to be started as soon as you have mastered Step 3 and can perform Step 3 in only a few seconds. Practice this as often as possible, until it becomes second nature to you.

1. Choose same movement or situation as in Step 3.

2. Take a few deep breaths.

3. Close your eyes.

4. Empty your mind.

5. Go to a quiet place in your mind.

6. Add to your body FEEL, the FEEL of the horse under you.
   FEEL your horse's barrel under your legs
   FEEL your horse's back
   FEEL your horse's elasticity
   FEEL your horse's neck
   FEEL your horse's mouth
   FEEL your horse's straightness
   FEEL your horse's rhythm
   FEEL your horse's relaxation
   FEEL your horse's responsiveness
   FEEL your horse's attitude
   FEEL your entire horse in relation to your being

7. Write a brief description of the experience. Be sure to note both what you felt easily and what was difficult for you to feel.
First try.

Second try.

Third try.

Fourth try.

Fifth try.

Sixth try.

RESOURCES-MOUNTAIN TOP

Questionnaire #17

Discovering Your Mountain Top

Put these ingredients together and discover your mountain top. If you are uncertain, take time to retreat to what you think is your mountain top and spend some time allowing yourself to evaluate how you feel after you have been there for ten minutes. If you feel calm, peaceful, and tranquil, you have found your mountain top.

Date:_____

	Calming	No Effect	Exciting
hacking in fields			
hacking in woods			
hacking along a stream			
alone in the stable			
feeding horses			
cleaning stalls			
grooming horse			
taking a shower			
taking a bath			
doing dishes			
cooking			
sauna			
whirlpool			
sitting by fire			
gurgling of stream			
quietness of pond			
powerful sound of waterfall			
sound of ocean			
gentle rush of river			
pounding of rapids			
moonlight			
sunlight			
darkness			
snow			
rain			
valley			
mountain			
listening to country & western music			
listening to hard or soft rock music			
listening to classical music			
listening to jazz music			
listening to new age music			
other			

RESOURCES -'ON HOLD'

Questionnaire #18

What Can I Put 'On Hold'

Date:_____

1. List all issues that you are trying to remember that have to do with your family.

2. List all the issues you are trying to remember that have to do with your job or with school.

3. List all the issues you are trying to remember that have to do with your horse.

4. List all the issues you are trying to remember that have to do with your social life.

5. List all the issues you are trying to remember that have to do with your community involvement.

6. List all the issues you must remember related to survival [buying clothes, groceries, personal doctor, dentist, etc].

RESOURCES-DISCIPLINE

Questionnaire #19

Self-Discipline Evaluation

Describe a situation in which you had to discipline yourself. Place a checkmark next to the phrases that describe your reactions in that situation. If you find that you have more checkmarks in the left column, your self-discipline is not appropriate. You need to make a closer examination of your role in your own discipline.

Date:_____

1. Describe a situation in which you had to discipline yourself. After you have described it, fill in the chart.

felt pressure from others	_____	felt satisfied	_____
felt pressure from self	_____	felt joy	_____
caused by expectations	_____	did best	_____
felt guilt	_____	felt relieved	_____
felt anger	_____	felt calm	_____
felt wronged	_____	saw own role	_____
felt empty	_____	felt fulfilled	_____

Date:_____

1. Describe a situation in which you had to discipline yourself. After you have described it, fill in the chart.

felt pressure from others	_____	felt satisfied	_____
felt pressure from self	_____	felt joy	_____
caused by expectations	_____	did best	_____
felt guilt	_____	felt relieved	_____
felt anger	_____	felt calm	_____
felt wronged	_____	saw own role	_____
felt empty	_____	felt fulfilled	_____

Remember, if you have more checkmarks in the left column, your self-discipline is not appropriate. You need to make a closer examination of your role in your own discipline.

RESOURCES-DISCIPLINE

Questionnaire #20

How Do I Use Discipline With Horses?

Describe a ride with your horse, and then check the description that best describes your reactions. The checkmarks in the right column need to be evaluated, because they indicate areas that need improvement.

Date:_____

1. Describe a ride.

physically relaxed	_____	physically tense	_____
mentally calm	_____	worried	_____
low anxiety	_____	anxious	_____
energized	_____	listless	_____
optimistic	_____	negative	_____
enjoyment	_____	discontent	_____
effortless	_____	tiring	_____
automatic	_____	required thought	_____
alert	_____	concentrated	_____
focused	_____	distracted	_____
self-confident	_____	inadequate	_____
in control of self	_____	controlled by envir.	_____

Date:_____

2. Describe a ride.

physically relaxed	_____	physically tense	_____
mentally calm	_____	worried	_____
low anxiety	_____	anxious	_____
energized	_____	listless	_____
optimistic	_____	negative	_____
enjoyment	_____	discontent	_____
effortless	_____	tiring	_____
automatic	_____	required thought	_____
alert	_____	concentrated	_____
focused	_____	distracted	_____
self-confident	_____	inadequate	_____
in control of self	_____	controlled by envir.	_____

RESOURCES-DISCIPLINE

Chart #3

Mental Training Practice

Month _____

Type of mental training _____

Our mounted time is our physical training time. Our mental training time is that time we spend on the mental aspects of riding while unmounted.

Physical and Mental Skill Practice Chart

	Minutes Practicing Physical	Minutes Practicing Mental
1		
2		
3		
4		
5		
6		
7		
8		
9		
10		
11		
12		
13		
14		
15		
16		
17		
18		
19		
20		
21		
22		
23		
24		
25		
26		
27		
28		
29		
30		
31		

RESOURCES-COMMITMENT

Questionnaire #21

Mapping Personal Commitment
Fill in your financial and time commitments in each area below.

Date:_____

Commitment Agreement

Commitment	Time/Day	$/Day

Education:
    school
    homework		

Job:
    quality of work
    hours of work		

Recreation: _____ [your choice]		

Family:
    spouse/partner
    children
    home care
    home management		

Community involvement: _____ [your choice]		
Social: _____ [Your choice]		

Horse:
    care
    practice
    competition		

See the following page for your Monthly Commitment Evaluation Chart.

In the following evaluation, honestly check whether you have fulfilled the commitment you made to each area. If you neglected more than 1/4 of the time, you should re-evaluate your commitments — perhaps they need readjusting.

Commitment Evaluation Chart

DAY	SCH.NEGL.	SCH.FULFILL	JOB NEGL.	JOB FULFILL	FAM.NEGL.	FAM.FULFILL	SOC. NEGL.	SOC.FULFILL	HORS.NEGL.	HORS.FULFILL
1										
2										
3										
4										
5										
6										
7										
8										
9										
10										
11										
12										
13										
14										
15										
16										
17										
18										
19										
20										
21										
22										
23										
24										
25										
26										
27										
28										
29										
30										
31										

RESOURCES-PRAISE

Chart #4

Mapping My Daily Praise

Date:_____

	#Times Praise Horse	#Times Praise Self	#Times Praise Others
1			
2			
3			
4			
5			
6			
7			
8			
9			
10			
11			
12			
13			
14			
15			
16			
17			
18			
19			
20			
21			
22			
23			
24			
25			
26			
27			
28			
29			
30			
31			

RESOURCES-PATIENCE

Questionnaire #22

What Interferes With Patience

To examine thoughts that can interfere with your patience, please rate from 1-3 [1 = often concerned about, 2 = average concern, 3 = seldom concerned about]. If you determine that you have answers of 2 or below more than a few times, you should evaluate your expectations and attitude. Perhaps your goals need to be changed.

Date:_____

Going to stable:

worried about weather	_____		not enough time	_____
late	_____		horse's attitude	_____

Riding:

worried about weather	_____		not enough time	_____
late	_____		horse's attitude	_____
other issues on mind	_____		future activities	_____
environment	_____		unexpected interf	_____

Instruction:

worried about weather	_____		not enough time	_____
late	_____		horse's attitude	_____
other issues on mind	_____		future activities	_____
environment	_____		unexpected interf	_____
instructor's opinion	_____		performance	_____

Competition:

worried about weather	_____		not enough time	_____
late	_____		horse's attitude	_____
other issues on mind	_____		future activities	_____
environment	_____		unexpected interf	_____
instructor's opinion	_____		performance	_____
other's opinions	_____		winning	_____

RESOURCES-FORGIVENESS

Questionnaire #23

Looking At My Horse's Forgiveness

Date:_____

1. Describe a situation in which your horse forgave you.

Describe how you felt afterward.

Date:_____

1. Describe a situation in which your horse forgave you.

Describe how you felt afterward.

Date:_____

3. Describe a situation in which your horse forgave you.

Describe how you felt afterward.

RESOURCES-FORGIVENESS

Questionnaire #24

Examining Forgiveness

Date:_____

1. During my childhood, who upset me, made me angry, or hurt me? Did I forgive them? If so, when?

2. During my pre-teen years, who upset me, made me angry, or hurt me? Did I forgive them? If so, when?

3. During my teenage years, who upset me, made me angry, or hurt me? Did I forgive them? If so, when?

4. During my young adult years, who upset me, made me angry, or hurt me? Did I forgive them? If so, when?

5. During my early adult years, who upset me, made me angry, or hurt me? Did I forgive them? If so, when?

6. During my middle-age years, who upset me, made me angry, or hurt me? Did I forgive them? If so, when?

7. During my late middle-age years, who upset me, made me angry, or hurt me? Did I forgive them? If so, when?

RESOURCES-IMAGERY AND VISUALIZATION

Exercise #5

Exercises To Improve Your Imagery

1. Choose a subject you want to learn. Describe it.

2. Investigate where you can observe what you have chosen to learn; someplace where you can see it being done correctly.

3. When you are ready to observe, review the subjects on your mind that you want to remember, and put them 'on hold'. What are they?

4. Go to the quiet place in your mind. Describe how you do this. By now you should have learned which way is best for you.

5. Notice any distractions, decide how to deal with them appropriately, and then do it. Describe.

6. Absorb yourself in the subject you have chosen to watch.

7. Review what you watched, and put it 'on hold'. Describe what you experienced; give a complete description, using all of your senses.

RESOURCES-IMAGERY AND VISUALIZATION

Exercise #6

Exercises To Practice Visualization

Four common uses of imagery and visualization: 1) Memorization, 2) Improve self-image, 3) Preparation for competition, 4) Daily practice

1. **Memorize Pattern:**
   recall all details cluttering your mind
   review them and put them 'on hold'
   empty your mind
   go to a quiet place in your mind
   recall the pattern with appropriate detail, using all senses
   review several times
   place 'on hold'
   move on

Describe the experience:

2. **Improve Self-Image:**
   recall all details cluttering your mind
   review them and put them 'on hold'
   empty your mind
   go to a quiet place in your mind
   recall problem feelings and images, try to replace them with
      appropriate POSITIVE feelings and images
   review several times
   place positive images 'on hold'

Describe the experience:

3. **Preparation For Competition:**
    recall all details cluttering your mind
    review them and put them 'on hold'
    empty your mind
    go to a quiet place in your mind
    view your expected, ideal performance at the competition site;
       include all environmental factors, and include all the best feelings
        that you have experienced.
    review several times
    place positive review 'on hold'

Once At The Competition:
    repeat exercise with actual site information

Just Prior To Performance:
    eliminate any distractions, including talking or listening to
       friends, family, coaches, etc.
    empty your mind
    go to your quiet place in your mind
    take a few deep breaths
    do a quick visualization review of the PERFECT performance,
       free from all distractions
    place 'on hold'
    Enter, Perform and ENJOY EACH MOMENT

Describe the experience:

4. **Practice Between Rides:**
    recall all details cluttering your mind
    review them and place 'on hold'
    empty your mind
    go to a quiet place in your mind
    recall your review of your last ride
    review it several times, complete with all senses
    place back 'on hold'
    move on
Describe the experience:

DISCOVERY

Everything you have read in *In Search of Your Image* and practiced in the Workbook has been designed to help you get to know and accept yourself better. The goal that inspired you to read this book, and me to write it, was to help horsepersons enjoy what they are doing by attaining the success that they desire. In the process, we may become happier, healthier people; with happy, sound horses. This last section will help you to evaluate the discoveries that you have made about yourself.

Understanding ourselves is an ongoing process. The process has just begun for you. It would be very good for you to review this Workbook in a year. You will find that by starting the process now, you will change and grow without much effort. If you answer the questionnaires next year without reviewing this year's answers, you may be in for a major SURPRISE! Those of you who would like to take on this challenge may want to plan ahead and order your next workbook now.

As I suggested before, answer the questionnaire at a time. The questions should be answered after some serious and honest soul-searching.

DISCOVERY-STRENGTHS AND WEAKNESSES

Questionnaire #1

While reading *In Search Of Your Image*, you may have discovered more about your own strengths and weaknesses. Please check discoveries that you have made, and on the next page add some of your own findings. Then indicate with a check mark what you are working on, have changed or accepted.

Date:_____

List	Working On	Changed	Accepted
I use goals daily	_____	_____	_____
I have accepted my physical body	_____	_____	_____
I love my body	_____	_____	_____
I love my horse's body	_____	_____	_____
I better understand my mind	_____	_____	_____
I understand my horse's mind	_____	_____	_____
I better understand my spirit	_____	_____	_____
I better understand my horse's spirit	_____	_____	_____
I love myself for who I am	_____	_____	_____
I love my horse for himself	_____	_____	_____
My energy matches my goals	_____	_____	_____
I feel my horse's energy	_____	_____	
I am humble	_____	_____	_____
I am egotistic	_____	_____	_____
I am a critical consumer	_____	_____	_____
I am a critical thinker	_____	_____	_____
I am a reflective thinker	_____	_____	_____
I can feel like a horse	_____	_____	_____
I can feel what others feel	_____	_____	_____
I can be physically relaxed	_____	_____	_____
I can be mentally relaxed	_____	_____	_____
I can concentrate	_____	_____	_____
I know my mountain top	_____	_____	_____
I use 'on hold'	_____	_____	_____
I am self-disciplined	_____	_____	_____
I honor commitments	_____	_____	_____
I make educated commitments	_____	_____	_____

I praise my horse often

I praise others often

I praise myself

I am patient with myself

I am patient with others

I am patient with my horse

I forgive and forget

I use imagery

I use visualization

I am decisive

I am aware

I create appropriate expectations

I communicate comfortably

I am a good listener

I can accept confrontation

I can confront when appropriate

I am responsible to my horse

I am responsible to others

I am responsible to myself

I am trusting

I can be trusted

I am appreciative

Your own evaluations:

DISCOVERY

Questionnaire #2

My Body, Mind and Spirit Connection

Our ability to engage our body, mind, and spirit in each activity is likely to produce better results. This questionnaire is designed to help you examine some of your routine activities and see if you do use all three parts together. If you do not, do not worry, your new awareness will allow you to use all of your assets in the future, when you are ready. Your body is involved in the action of most of these situations. You know if your mind is involved if you think. Whenever you feel, whether with your body or with your mind, you are involving your spirit. I have not included any negative statements, because I am hoping that each participant has a positive attitude. If you feel negative, leave it blank or fill in the negative feeling. If you view the experience negatively too often, I suggest that you reevaluate your goals and related activities.

Date:_____

	Body	**Mind**	**Spirit**
1. When you go to the stable do you:			
Praise others often	_____	_____	_____
Feel energetic	_____	_____	_____
Feel your horse's gladness	_____	_____	_____
Think about what you are going to do	_____	_____	_____
Think about how your horse feels	_____	_____	_____
Enjoy the experience of going	_____	_____	_____
Finish the task with a good feeling	_____	_____	_____
2. While you are preparing your horse to ride, do you:			
Feel enthusiastic	_____	_____	_____
Feel tired	_____	_____	_____
Feel aches and pains in body	_____	_____	_____
Notice horse's behavior	_____	_____	_____
Think about horse's body reactions	_____	_____	_____
Feel horse's body responses	_____	_____	_____
Think about your last ride	_____	_____	_____
Think about today's ride	_____	_____	_____
Enjoy the preparatory experience	_____	_____	_____
3. During your warm-up, do you:			
Think about your program	_____	_____	_____
Feel each joint of your body	_____	_____	_____
Feel your horse's body	_____	_____	_____
Evaluate your body's suppleness	_____	_____	_____
Evaluate your horse's warm-up	_____	_____	_____
Use your evaluation to create today's ride	_____	_____	_____

4. During the ride itself, do you:

Plan a program based on warm-up and
intermediate training program   _____ _____ _____

Feel the need to make a correction   _____ _____ _____

Feel a need to do something
but not sure what   _____ _____ _____

Think about what you are
doing every moment   _____ _____ _____

Think after you feel
you need something   _____ _____ _____

Take action then think   _____ _____ _____

Feel your horse's movement   _____ _____ _____

Feel your own movement   _____ _____ _____

Feel your horse's mood   _____ _____ _____

Feel your own mood   _____ _____ _____

Evaluate your horse's mood   _____ _____ _____

Evaluate your own mood   _____ _____ _____

Relate mood to goal of day   _____ _____ _____

Enjoy the interaction
between self and horse   _____ _____ _____

Feel energized   _____ _____ _____

Feel tired   _____ _____ _____

Think you achieved something   _____ _____ _____

Determine tomorrow's program   _____ _____ _____

5. During your untacking and clean up time, do you:

Think about how your horse feels   _____ _____ _____

Feel your horse's reactions   _____ _____ _____

Notice your horse's body condition   _____ _____ _____

Notice your horse's attitude   _____ _____ _____

Feel your own energy   _____ _____ _____

Feel satisfied with what you achieved   _____ _____ _____

Think you are satisfied
with day's experience   _____ _____ _____

Enjoyed your time with your horse   _____ _____ _____

Feel glad you spent the time   _____ _____ _____

Feel ready to be attentive
to your next task   _____ _____ _____

6. On your way to the next activity, do you:

Feel tired   _____ _____ _____

Feel confident   _____ _____ _____

Feel enthusiasm   _____ _____ _____

Think about your next task   _____ _____ _____

Review and relive today's horse activity _____ _____ _____

Feel like singing or enjoying music   _____ _____ _____

Feel satisfied   _____ _____ _____

Enjoy the environment of the drive   _____ _____ _____

DISCOVERY

Questionnaire #3

What I Enjoy The Most

From your mountain top, review your horse activities. Recall the activities that have made you feel the best. A satisfying experience is an indication of inner balance. If your experiences are only OK, perhaps something is missing. This questionnaire may help you find the missing ingredient. Check the appropriate feelings of satisfaction. "Good" includes feelings of satisfaction, tranquility, accomplishment, energy and harmony.

Date:_____

	No Effect	OK	Good
1. How I feel when:			
I think about horse care	_____	_____	_____
I think about my riding	_____	_____	_____
I care for my horse	_____	_____	_____
I ride in the ring	_____	_____	_____
I have a lesson	_____	_____	_____
I ride in the country	_____	_____	_____
I plan a competition	_____	_____	_____
I prepare for a competition	_____	_____	_____
I compete	_____	_____	_____
After the competition	_____	_____	_____
While watching a competition	_____	_____	_____
While watching a horse in stall	_____	_____	_____
While watching a horse run free	_____	_____	_____

2. Describe, in detail, an activity that made you feel really good.

3. Check any of the following that describe feelings that you had:

accomplishment   _____

feeling horse   _____

empathy with horse   _____

achieving goal   _____

winning   _____

pride   _____

joy   _____

satisfaction   _____

companionship   _____

confidence   _____

understanding   _____

inner awareness   _____

acceptance   _____

happiness   _____

fun   _____

Now look at your answers and decide which factors influenced your positive feelings. What made you feel good, planning the activity, the activity itself, or the results of the activity? What you conclude does not matter, what is important is recognizing what makes you feel good so that you can enjoy it and do more of it! It is important to have pleasurable experiences and it is fun to know what makes them pleasurable, because you may be able to discover some pleasure in some unpleasant tasks, or you may be able to use the pleasure as a reward for an unpleasant task.

DISCOVERY

Questionnaire #4

Positive vs Negative

     Answer the following questions as honestly as you can. They will help you examine your attitude. Is it honest? Is it positive? If you identify the negative, you may be able to achieve more success.

Date:_____

1. No matter what I do, I do not feel good enough at doing it.
     Why do I feel this way?

     What would be the result if I thought and felt I could do it?

     Are my expectations realistic?

2. I want my friends and associates to think I can do what I am setting out to do, but I really "know" that I cannot do it.
     Why am I pretending?

     What would happen if I told my friends how I really felt?

     Can I really do it or not? If not, why can't I?

3. I should have achieved my goal by now.
    Why do I think that?

    What are the reasons for not achieving it yet?

    What will happen because I have not achieved it on my time
    schedule?

4. It is wrong to do something just because I enjoy it myself.
    Why do I believe this?

    What is wrong with allowing myself to feel good?

    What happens when I feel good about myself?

5. I must present myself as having the same ideals as those in my stable or club.
    Why do I think this?

    Do I really know other people's ideals or am I assuming that I know them?

    What is wrong with having my own ideals?

    What will happen if I pursue my own ideals?

6. I cannot show others how much I love my horse.
   Why do I feel that way?

   What will happen if I do show the depths of my love?

   What is wrong with showing love?

7. I cannot let others know that I am investigating trainers and instructors.
   Why do I feel this way?

   What will happen if they know?

   What is wrong with investigation?

8. When something bad happens to my horse, I:
   blame myself   _____
   blame my horse   _____
   blame my professional   _____
   blame the environment   _____
   Look at all possibilities   _____

9. When I have a bad riding experience, I:
   blame myself   _____
   blame my horse   _____
   blame my professional   _____
   blame the environment   _____
   Look at all possibilities   _____

10. When I have a wonderful experience, I:
    credit my horse   _____
    credit my instructor   _____
    credit myself   _____
    am afraid to enjoy it   _____
    think it was a coincidence   _____

DISCOVERY

Questionnaire #5

The 'Now' and Me

Date:_____

1. Recall a recent trip to the stable:
    What was I thinking about?

    What was I feeling?

    What do I remember most about the trip?

Date:_____

2. Recall a recent preparation for a ride:
    What was I thinking about?

    What was I feeling?

    What do I remember most about the preparation?

Date:_____

3. Recall a recent ride in the ring:
    Was I thinking or feeling more?

    What was I thinking or feeling?

    What do I remember most about my ride?

Date:_____

4. Recall a recent lesson:
    Was I listening most to my horse, my instructor, or my self?

    What was the main focus of my lesson?

    What did I gain from the lesson?

Date:_____

5. Recall a recent ride in the country:
    What was I thinking about?

    What was I feeling?

    What do I remember most from that ride?

Date:_____

6. Recall putting horse away after a ride:
    What was I thinking about?

    What was I feeling?

    What do I remember most?

Date:_____

7. Recall a recent trip after a ride:
    What was I thinking about?

    What was I feeling?

    What do I remember most about that trip?

DISCOVERY

Questionnaire #6

The Role Of My Goals

Our goals can create the map for our feelings of success. You may have discovered that your goals are appropriate, that you have not used goals, or that your goals are not appropriate for all factors in your life. The following questions will help you to identify where you are at the moment in relation to your use of riding goals.

Date:_____

1. The long-term goal I have discovered:

2. My intermediate goals to meet to work toward my long-term goal.

3. My short-term goals to meet my intermediate goal.

1. Rate the following statements by placing a check mark in OK if the answers were satisfactory in the past, and in Changed if you made a change.

Statement:	OK	Changed
Fulfillment		
My motivation is realistic		
My goals are appropriate for my stage in life		
My time available balances with my goal		
My energy level balances with my goal		
My financial situation balances with my goal		
My long-term goal is realistic		
My intermediate goal is appropriate to help me work toward my long-term goal		
My short-term goal is appropriate to help me meet my intermediate goal		

2. To discover what using your goals does for you, rate the following with a check mark.

Feeling:	Good	Frustrated
satisfaction		
fulfillment		
energized		
confidence		
enthusiasm		
meeting daily goal		
confronting roadblocks		
honoring commitment		
making decisions		
communication with horse		
communication with instructor		
communications with student		
inspired		

DISCOVERY

Questionnaire #7

Who Am I?

Please rate the following statements according to what feels closest to what you believe about yourself. Further examination should go into the checkmarks under rejection or uncertainty.

Date:_____

Statement:	Accept	Uncertain	Reject
I can accept my insecurity, fear, pain, and problems that I cannot change.	_____	_____	_____
I must change, and will change what I can change.	_____	_____	_____
I must stop wasting energy on the negatives and look at the positive.	_____	_____	_____
I want to balance my body, mind, and spirit.	_____	_____	_____
It is OK to be myself and not try to fool those around me.	_____	_____	_____
If I look at a time I felt embarrassed, what would have happened if I had accepted the embarrassment with humor? Can I accept embarrassment?	_____	_____	_____
If I look at times when I felt humiliated, what would have happened if I had accepted my mistake and moved on? Can I accept humiliation?	_____	_____	_____
If I look at a time when I felt ashamed, what would have happened if I had accepted the feeling and moved on? Can I accept feeling ashamed?	_____	_____	_____
Could I have been accepting when I felt defensive with horse or man?	_____	_____	_____
Could I have felt accepting when I felt like blaming horse or man?	_____	_____	_____

Statement:	Accept	Uncertain	Reject
When I feel that I am a victim, do I accept or reject?	_____	_____	_____
When something goes wrong, do I feel like challenging and improving?	_____	_____	_____
I enjoy the reward of the experience itself.	_____	_____	_____
I need the result to feel good about an experience.	_____	_____	_____
I am willing to challenge my beliefs.	_____	_____	_____
I believe that a crisis can create a rewarding experience.	_____	_____	_____
I have experienced a crisis creating positive results.	_____	_____	_____
I can see the importance of my life in relationship to life itself.	_____	_____	_____
My life feels full.	_____	_____	_____
I feel the value of meditation.	_____	_____	_____
I feel the value of my life with my horse.	_____	_____	_____
I feel the value of my life in my stable.	_____	_____	_____
I feel the value of my life with other people.	_____	_____	_____
I feel the value of my life in the horse community.	_____	_____	_____
I feel the value of being a positive, inspirational role model.	_____	_____	_____
I feel the importance of humility, interacting honestly with those with whom I come in contact.	_____	_____	_____
I take time to dream, ponder, and appreciate life.	_____	_____	_____

Statement:	Accept	Uncertain	Reject
I trust and accept my intuition.	_____	_____	_____
I want to continue to learn.	_____	_____	_____
I use my critical thinking process freely.	_____	_____	_____
I use my reflective thinking process freely.	_____	_____	_____
I easily empathize with my horse.	_____	_____	_____
I try to understand the other before reacting.	_____	_____	_____
I try to communicate completely so the other being understands and I understand.	_____	_____	_____
I try to balance the demands on my life.	_____	_____	_____
I try to balance what I give to myself, others, and community.	_____	_____	_____
I can create daily realistic goals and feel the satisfaction at the end of the day.	_____	_____	_____
I feel I can listen to my inner feelings, and take time to do this when they present themselves to me.	_____	_____	_____
I accept others' desire to fulfill their potential.	_____	_____	_____
I do not expect others to feel or think like myself.	_____	_____	_____
I do not expect myself to feel or think like others around me.	_____	_____	_____
I trust others until they prove me wrong.	_____	_____	_____
I trust myself but remain my own best critic.	_____	_____	_____
I trust my need to be involved beyond my own being, to be a positive participant in the world around me.	_____	_____	_____

My Personal Journal

Fill in date and important information. Include both facts and feelings.

Date:_____

_____

_____

_____

_____

_____

_____

_____

_____

_____

_____

_____

_____

_____

_____

_____

_____

Date:_____

_____

_____

_____

_____

_____

_____

_____

_____

_____

_____

_____

_____

_____

_____

_____

_____

_____

_____

Date:_____

_____

_____

_____

_____

_____

_____

_____

_____

_____

_____

_____

_____

_____

_____

_____

_____

_____

_____